Meg Parker
and
Mystery at the Red Barn

Eleanor Robins

High Noon Books
Novato, California

Cover Design: Nancy Peach
Interior Illustrations: Herb Heidinger

International Standard Book Number: 0-87879-474-3

8 7 6 5 4 3 2 1 0 9
3 2 1 0 9 8 7 6 5 4

You'll enjoy all the High Noon Books
Write for a free full list of titles.

Contents

CHAPTER 1

Friday Afternoon

Meg and Kate were walking down the steps at school. Dave and Fred were walking with them. Dave was Meg's boy friend. And Kate liked Fred a lot.

The four were on their way to Meg's car in the school parking lot.

"I sure am glad school is over for this week," Kate said.

Meg said, "I am, too. I'm always glad when Friday afternoon comes."

"I'm really glad Friday afternoon is here this week," Kate said.

"Why?" Fred asked.

"Because Mom and Dad are going out of town. And I'm going to stay with Meg the next two nights," Kate answered.

Dave said, "I wish the four of us could do something together tomorrow afternoon. But Fred and I have to work at the Ice Cream Shop. What are you girls going to do tomorrow?"

"We're going out to the Red Barn to ride horses," Meg answered.

The Red Barn was a horse farm. It was a long way from town.

"When are you going?" Dave asked.

"Maybe after lunch," Meg said.

Dave laughed. "I'm sure you girls won't go before lunch tomorrow," he said.

"How can you be so sure, Dave?" Meg asked. She didn't know when they were going. So how could he know?

"I know you girls too well. You'll be up all night talking. Then you'll sleep all morning. Maybe even part of the afternoon. And Fred and I will be working very hard," Dave answered.

Meg laughed. Then she said, "You don't work that hard, Dave. And you're wrong. Kate and I won't be up all night talking. Just most of the night. And part of that time we're going to be doing some work for school."

3

The four walked up to Meg's old green car.

Meg opened the door on her side of the car. Kate opened the door on her side. Then both girls got in the car.

"I was going to call you tonight, Meg. But I don't think you'll have time to talk to me," Dave said.

"Dave, you know I always have time to talk to you," Meg said.

Dave smiled. He said, "I thought you'd say that. I'll call you tonight around 7:00."

"OK," Meg said.

The boys started walking to Dave's white car.

CHAPTER 2

Put Your Money Away

"Where to now, Meg? Your house?" Kate asked.

Meg said, "No. We have to stop by the grocery store. Mom asked me to get some things for us to eat tonight. And I told her I would."

Meg started her car. She looked to see if any cars were coming. She didn't see any. Then she started driving out of the school parking lot.

"I sure hope we can get all our studying done tonight. Then we won't have any to do tomorrow night," Kate said.

"Maybe we can. But we'll have to work hard," Meg said.

"That's OK. I just don't want to have any work to do tomorrow night," Kate said.

"Why? Do you have some plans I don't know about?" Meg asked.

"No. But maybe we will by tomorrow night," Kate said.

"Like what?" Meg asked.

"Didn't Dave say he was going to call you tonight?" Kate asked.

"Yes," Meg answered. She wondered what that had to do with what Kate was talking about.

"You could ask him to come over to your house tomorrow night. And you could ask him to bring Fred, too. I know it would be OK with your mom and dad. Will you ask him?" Kate said.

"OK. But they might already have other plans," Meg said.

"Thanks, Meg," Kate said.

Meg turned into the parking lot at the grocery store. She parked her car.

Meg and Kate hurried into the grocery store. They quickly got the things that Meg's mom wanted. Then they got in line to pay for everything.

A tall man and a short man were in front of the girls. The short man started to pay for what he and the other man were buying.

The tall man said, "Put your money away. I'm paying for everything."

"You don't have to. I have a $20 bill," the short man said. He showed the man his $20 bill.

The tall man looked mad. He said, "I told you to put your money away. I told you that I'm going to pay for everything."

"No, I'm going to. You can pay the next time," the short man said.

The tall man looked even madder. He said, "I told you that I was going to pay for everything. So put your money away."

"Don't talk so loudly. People are looking at us," the other man said.

The tall man didn't say anything else. He let

the short man pay for everything. Then the two men left the grocery store. The tall man seemed to be in a hurry to go. But the short man walked slowly.

Kate said, "I wonder why that tall man didn't want the other man to pay for everything. Most people are glad for other people to pay for everything."

"But maybe he isn't like that," Meg said.

Meg quickly paid for what she was buying. Then she and Kate hurried out of the store.

The girls started walking to Meg's car. The two men were walking in front of them. The two men were talking so loudly that the girls could hear what they were saying.

"You should have let me pay for everything," the tall man said.

"I don't know why you're mad. You should

"Because of you the police might find out what we're doing here," the tall man said.

be glad that I had that $20 bill with me," the short man said.

"Because of you the police might find out what we're doing here. And we aren't ready to move on yet," the tall man said.

The short man said, "I didn't even think about that. We'd better get away from this grocery store as fast as we can."

The two men hurried over to a brown car. They got in the car. They quickly rode out of the parking lot.

Meg and Kate forgot to look at the tag number on their car.

CHAPTER 3

Meg Helps

"Did you hear what that tall man said, Meg?" Kate asked.

"I sure did," Meg answered.

"I wonder what he was talking about," Kate said.

Meg was wondering the same thing. She said, "I don't know. But I think I should call my Uncle Bob. I think he should know what the man said."

"I think he should, too," Kate said.

Meg and Kate hurried to a pay phone.

Meg gave Kate the sack she was carrying. Then she called the Police Station.

Meg said, "This is Meg Parker. I want to talk to my Uncle Bob."

Meg's Uncle Bob was the Police Chief. He was also the brother of Meg's dad.

Meg's uncle came to the phone. Meg told him all about the two men.

Then Meg said, "Do you know what they might be doing here?"

Her uncle said, "I have an idea. But I need to go to the grocery store to make sure before I tell you. Do you know where the two men are now?"

"No, I don't. They rode off in a brown car. But I forgot to get their car tag number," Meg said.

Her uncle said, "That's OK, Meg. You've been a big help. I'm going over to the grocery store now. I'll call you later at your house."

"OK, Uncle Bob. I hope you find out what the two men are doing here," Meg said.

Meg told Kate what her uncle had said. Then the two girls hurried to Meg's car.

It wasn't very long before the girls got to Meg's house. They quickly got out of the car.

Meg said, "I'll carry the sack of things we got at the grocery store. And you can take our school books in the house."

14

"OK," Kate said.

The girls hurried into Meg's house.

Meg's mom called to her from the kitchen. She said, "Is that you, Meg?"

"Yes, Mom," Meg answered.

Meg and Kate went into the kitchen. Meg gave the sack to her mom. Then she and Kate went up to her room. Kate put their school books on Meg's desk.

Kate said, "I sure am glad your little sister Amy is staying with a friend of hers tonight."

"So am I. I hope she has a good time," Meg said.

The phone rang. Meg hoped her Uncle Bob was calling her.

CHAPTER 4

Three Phone Calls

A few minutes later Meg's mom called up the steps to her. She said, "Meg, your Uncle Bob wants to talk to you."

Meg hurried to answer the phone.

"Did you find out what the two men are doing here, Uncle Bob?" Meg asked.

Her uncle said, "I sure did. The short man passed a fake $20 bill at the grocery store. I knew two men had been doing that in other towns near here. But I didn't know they had come here."

"I'm glad you found out what they are doing here. I wish we knew where they were now," Meg said.

Meg told her mom and Kate what her uncle had said.

Her uncle said, "So do I. Thank you for telling me about the two men. I'm going to tell all the store owners to look for fake $20 bills. And my policemen will look for the two men."

"Thanks for calling to tell me what was going on," Meg said.

Meg told her mom and Kate what her uncle had said. Both were very surprised.

A little later Meg's dad came home. Meg told him all about the men while they were all eating. Her dad was very surprised, too.

They finished eating. Then Meg said, "Kate and I will clean up the kitchen, Mom."

"That's very nice of you, Meg. But don't you two have a lot of school work?" her mom asked.

"We can do it later, Mrs. Parker," Kate said.

"Then I'll be very glad for you girls to clean up," Meg's mom said.

Meg's mom and dad went into the den. Meg and Kate started to clean up the kitchen.

The phone rang.

Kate said, "That must be Dave. Don't forget to ask him to bring Fred over here tomorrow night."

"I won't," Meg said.

Meg and Dave talked for a few minutes. Meg told him about the two men at the grocery store. And she told him that the short man passed a fake $20 bill. Dave was very surprised. They talked for a few more minutes.

Then Meg said, "Would you like to come over here tomorrow night?"

Dave said, "You know I would. But I thought Kate was going to be there."

"She is. But you could ask Fred to come with you," Meg said.

Dave laughed. Then he said, "Now I know why you asked me to come. Kate wants me to talk Fred into coming to see her. I'll call Fred right now. And I'll call you back in a few minutes."

Meg told Kate what Dave said.

The girls finished cleaning up the kitchen. Then they sat down at the kitchen table. It wasn't very long before Dave called.

"What did Fred say?" Meg asked.

"He said he would come with me. So we'll see you tomorrow night around 7:00," Dave said.

"Great. See you then," Meg said.

Meg told Kate what Dave said.

Kate got very excited. She said, "I can hardly wait. Let's hurry up to your room. I want to get started on our school work right away. I want to have everything finished before we go to bed. Then we'll have a lot of time tomorrow to get ready for the boys to come."

Meg told her mom and dad that the boys were coming over the next night. Then she and Kate hurried up to her room. They had a lot to do.

They worked for a long time on their school work. It was very late when they finished all of it. Then Kate wanted to talk about Fred.

"We need to stop talking and go to bed. We need to get some sleep. Or we won't feel like getting up tomorrow morning," Meg said.

Meg turned off the lights. It wasn't long before she and Kate went to sleep.

CHAPTER 5

Stay Away From There!

Kate woke up early the next morning. She was very excited about Fred planning to come over to Meg's house that night.

Kate quickly got out of bed. Then she said, "Wake up, Meg. It's time to get up."

Meg was still tired because she stayed up so late. She said, "Why do we have to get up so early, Kate?"

"So we can go to the Red Barn this morning," Kate answered.

"We have all day to do that. We don't have to go out there this morning," Meg said.

Kate said, "I won't have time to go out there this afternoon."

"Why not?" Meg asked.

"I have to wash my hair. And I have to wash my best blouse. And I have a lot of other things to do before Fred comes tonight," Kate said.

Meg laughed. Then she said, "I know, Kate. You want to take all afternoon to get ready. But you want to look like you got ready at the last minute."

Kate laughed. Then she said, "Is it OK with you to go out to the Red Barn this morning?"

"It is now that I know why you want to go

this morning," Meg said.

The girls got ready to go out to the Red Barn. They ate breakfast. Then they hurried out to Meg's old green car.

Soon they were on their way to the Red Barn.

Kate said, "I sure am excited about tonight. But I know it isn't really a date."

"I think it's a date. Fred didn't have to say he'd come over tonight. I think he wants to be with you," Meg said.

"I sure hope you're right," Kate said.

"I'm sure I am," Meg said.

Kate had a big smile on her face. Meg was glad her friend was happy.

Meg said, "I hope Uncle Bob can find those two men today. I sure wish I'd gotten the tag number of their brown car."

"What do you want?" the man asked.
He didn't look pleased.

"I wish we had, too," Kate said.

It took a long time to get to the Red Barn.

Meg parked her car next to a brown car. She and Kate got out of her car.

A man in a red shirt came out of the barn. He hurried over to them. Meg had never seen him before.

"What do you want?" the man asked. He didn't look pleased to see them.

"We're here to ride the horses," Meg said.

"You can't ride them today," the man said.

"Why not?" Kate asked.

"Because I said you couldn't," the man said.

"Where is Mr. Page, the owner?" Meg asked.

"He isn't here. He had to go out of town for a few days," the man answered.

"Mr. Page would let us ride the horses. He always does. We come out here a lot," Kate said.

"Then come back next week when Mr. Page is here. You can ride the horses then," the man said.

"OK. We'll come back next week," Meg said.

Kate said, "I still don't know why you won't let us ride the horses. I'm going in the barn to see them before we go."

Kate started walking to the barn.

"Stay away from that barn," the man said.

CHAPTER 6

Stop Right There!

Kate was very surprised. She stopped walking to the barn. She said, "Why can't I go and see the horses?"

"Because I told you not to," the man said.

"Kate isn't going to do anything to the horses. She just wants to see them," Meg said.

The man said, "That's what you say. How do I know she wouldn't do something to them? And it's my job to take good care of the horses while Mr. Page is gone."

Meg saw a man look out of a window of the barn. She thought she had seen the man before. And she thought about the brown car next to her car.

Meg said, "Come on, Kate. Let's go. Maybe we can come back next week and ride the horses."

Kate stayed right where she was. She said, "I'm not ready to go."

"But I am. So let's go," Meg said. She wanted to get away from there as fast as they could.

"All right," Kate said. But she wasn't happy about going. She slowly started walking with Meg to Meg's car.

The man looked very glad to see them go.

Meg quickly got in her car. Kate slowly got in the car.

Kate said, "I don't know why you said we had to go. You shouldn't have let that man run us off. It would have been OK with Mr. Page for me to go in the barn."

"I know, Kate," Meg said. Then she started her car and drove away from the Red Barn.

Kate said, "You should have let me stay. I'm sure I could have made that man let me see the horses."

"I don't think you could have, Kate. I don't think he would have let us get anywhere near the barn," Meg said.

Meg pulled off the road. She stopped her car next to some trees.

Kate was very surprised. She said, "Why did you stop here, Meg?"

"So we can leave my car here. Then we're going to walk back to the Red Barn," Meg said.

"Why are we going to do that?" Kate asked.

"I saw a man look out one of the windows of the barn. I think I've seen the man before. I think he was the tall man we saw at the grocery store. And I think the brown car there was the car we saw him ride away in. I want to go back and try to find out," Meg said.

Kate was very surprised. She said, "I knew you didn't let that man run us off, Meg."

The girls got out of Meg's car. Then they started walking back to the Red Barn.

"Stay next to the trees, Kate," Meg said.

"Why?" Kate asked.

"We don't want anyone at the Red Barn to see us," Meg answered.

"I'm glad you thought of that," Kate said.

Soon the girls could see the Red Barn. They walked next to the trees as long as they could. They didn't see anyone outside of the barn.

"Maybe we can get next to the barn without anyone seeing us. Then we can look inside it. But we have to be very careful. We don't want anyone to see us," Meg said.

"I'll be careful," Kate said.

The girls walked over to the side of the barn.

No one saw them. They looked inside the barn.

They saw two men. One was the man in the

The girls walked over to the side
of the barn. They looked inside.

34

red shirt. The other was the tall man they had seen at the grocery store. The girls didn't see the short man anywhere.

The two men were very busy. They were making fake money.

"Meg, that is the tall man we saw at the grocery store. And look what he and the man in the red shirt are doing. They're making fake money. That's why that man didn't want me to go in the barn," Kate said.

"Be quiet, Kate," Meg said. She pulled her friend away from the window.

Meg hoped the men inside the barn hadn't heard Kate.

Meg pulled Kate away from the barn.

Then Meg said in a low voice, "Come on, Kate. We have to get back to my car as fast as we can. I need to drive to a phone. I need to call Uncle Bob right away."

"Let's go," Kate said.

The girls started hurrying away.

A man's voice said, "Stop right where you are, girls."

CHAPTER 7

Meg Needs Help

Meg and Kate quickly stopped.

Kate said, "What are we going to do, Meg?"

"Be quiet, Kate. Let me do all the talking," Meg said.

The girls turned around to see who had told them to stop. It was the short man they had seen at the grocery store. He looked mad.

"What are you doing here?" the man asked.

Meg had to think very quickly about what to say. She said, "We're here to use your phone."

"Why? And how did you get here?" the man asked.

Meg said, "We came out here in my car to ride the horses. But a man in a red shirt said we couldn't ride them today. He said we would have to come back next week when Mr. Page is here."

"So why are you here now?" the man asked.

Meg said, "My car ran out of gas not far from here. We walked back here to call my Uncle Bob to bring us some gas. Is it OK to use your phone? Then we can walk back to my car. We can wait there for my uncle to come."

"All right. Come with me," the man said.

The girls followed him into the office at the Red Barn.

Meg called the Police Station. She hoped her uncle was there. And she hoped she would be able to let him know something was wrong.

A policeman answered the phone.

Meg said, "This is Meg Parker. I must talk to my Uncle Bob right away."

"Hold on," the policeman said.

Soon Meg's uncle came to the phone. He said, "Is something wrong, Meg?"

"I'm out at the Red Barn. My car ran out of gas. I need you to bring me some gas right away," Meg said.

"I can't leave the Police Station right now. But I can call a gas station for you. Someone there can bring you some gas," her uncle said.

"But Mom isn't home right now, Uncle Bob. That's why you have to bring the gas to me. No one else can bring it to me," Meg said. She hoped

The short man said, "Hurry up, kid. You can't talk on the phone all day."

her uncle would know something was very wrong.

"Is something going on out there that I should know about?" her uncle asked.

"Yes, Uncle Bob," Meg said.

The short man said, "Hurry up, kid. You can't talk on the phone all day."

"I have to hang up now, Uncle Bob. Kate and I will wait for you at my car. It's not far down the road from the Red Barn," Meg said.

Meg hung up. She hoped the short man would let her and Kate go back to her car.

CHAPTER 8

Uncle Bob Comes

The short man said, "I let you use the phone. Now get out of here and get back to your car."

Meg and Kate hurried out of the office. They hurried away from the Red Barn as fast as they could.

Meg said, "I hope Uncle Bob comes soon. I don't want the men to leave before he gets here."

The girls waited for Meg's uncle at her car. It seemed a long time before they saw two police cars coming down the road.

The two police cars stopped near them.

Meg's uncle got out of his car. "What's going on at the Red Barn? Why did you say I needed to come out here?"

Meg told her uncle about seeing the two men again. And she told him about the men making fake money in the barn.

Meg's uncle quickly drove away. The other police car followed his car.

A long time later Meg and Kate saw the two police cars coming back. The two police cars stopped near the girls.

The man in the red shirt was in the back of the car Meg's uncle was driving. The tall man and the short man were in the back of the other car.

Meg's uncle said, "Thank you for all your help, girls. We got the men and what they used to make the fake money. Another man who works at the Red Barn said you can ride the horses now. He didn't know what was going on in the barn."

Kate said, "We don't have time to ride the horses now."

Meg knew Kate wanted to start getting ready for Fred to come. She said, "Come on, Kate. Let's go. I want you to be sure to have time to get everything done."

Both girls had smiles on their faces as they walked back to Meg's car.